Violin Exam Pieces

ABRSM Grade 3

Selected from the 2016–2019 syllabus

Name

Date of exam

D0417161

Contents

page

Violin consultant: Philippa Bunting
Footnotes: Richard Jones (RJ) and Anthony Burton

Other pieces for Grade 3

LIST A

4 **J. S. Bach** Gavotte 1 (from Gavotte in D). No. 6 from *Suzuki Violin School*, Vol. 3 (Alfred–Summy-Birchard)

5 **F. Duval** Un peu gay. No. 3 from *My First Concert* for Violin, arr. Mohrs (Schott)

6 **Handel** Bourrée: No. 11 from *The Young Violinist's Repertoire*, Book 4, arr. de Keyser and Waterman (Faber)

LIST B

4 **Neil Mackay** German Folk Song *and* Swiss Air: from *A Tuneful Introduction to the Third Position* (Stainer & Bell)

5 **Moniuszko** Baika. No. 3 from *The Young Violinist's Repertoire*, Book 4, arr. de Keyser and Waterman (Faber)

6 **J. Strauss II** The Beautiful Blue Danube (*violin melody*) (*omitting DC*). from *The Viennese Fiddler*, arr. Huws Jones (Boosey & Hawkes)

LIST C

4 **Roy McCormack** Louis: No. 10 from *Let's Swing* for Violin (Spartan Press)

5 **Monty Norman** James Bond Theme. *James Bond 007 Collection* for Violin, arr. Galliford, Neuburg and Edmondson (Alfred)

6 **Ros Stephen** Tango in San Telmo *or* African Jamboree: No. 7 *or* No. 12 from *Violin Globetrotters* (OUP)

First published in 2015 by ABRSM (Publishing) Ltd, a wholly owned subsidiary of ABRSM, 24 Portland Place, London W1B 1LU, United Kingdom

Music origination by Andrew Jones
Cover by Kate Benjamin & Andy Potts
Printed in England by Caligraving Ltd, Thetford, Norfolk

A:1

Pastime with good company

Arranged by Edward Huws Jones

attrib. Henry VIII
(1491–1547)

This song, originally for three voices, has survived in a manuscript compiled around 1518 at the court of the English King Henry VIII. Like many other pieces in the same collection, it is ascribed to the King himself, a keen music-lover who is known to have been a composer. Henry, still young at the time, probably also wrote the carefree words, which begin:

Pastime with good company
I love and shall until I die

This arrangement includes a second verse with violin 'divisions', or decorative variation, of the kind that a performer at the time might have improvised. Although the original metronome mark is ♩ = 100, a more relaxed tempo of ♩ = *c*.84 would be acceptable in the exam.

Polonaise

No. 4 from 12 Duos, K. 487

Arranged by Watson Forbes

W. A. Mozart
(1756–91)

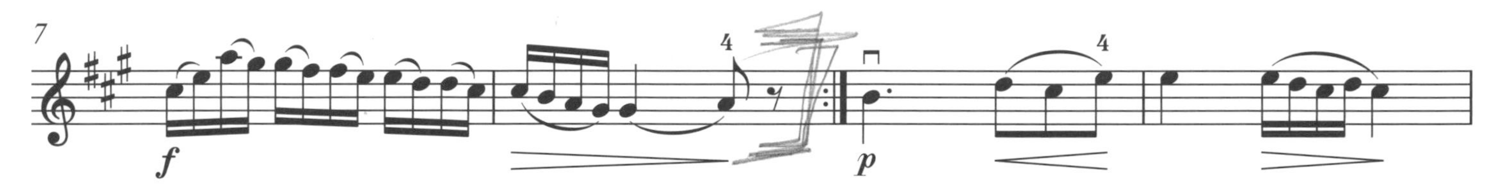

Mozart composed a set of 12 short duos for two equal instruments in Vienna in July 1786; on the surviving manuscript of three of them he noted that they were written 'while playing skittles', but failed to identify the instruments they were intended for. They were published after Mozart's death as pieces for two horns, and indeed they can be played on the valveless horns of the time, using the high-register technique associated with the instrument. But for many years it was believed that they were too difficult for horns, and they were published most frequently as duos for violins. The fourth of the set is in the rhythm of the polonaise, a triple-time dance from Poland (the name is the French for 'Polish') made famous in the 19th century by Chopin's piano polonaises. This arrangement includes the second horn, or violin, part in the piano accompaniment, sometimes in the left hand and sometimes in the right.

Presto

Third movement from Sonatina No. 6 in F, TWV 41:F1

Edited by and continuo realization by Richard Jones

G. P. Telemann (1681–1767)

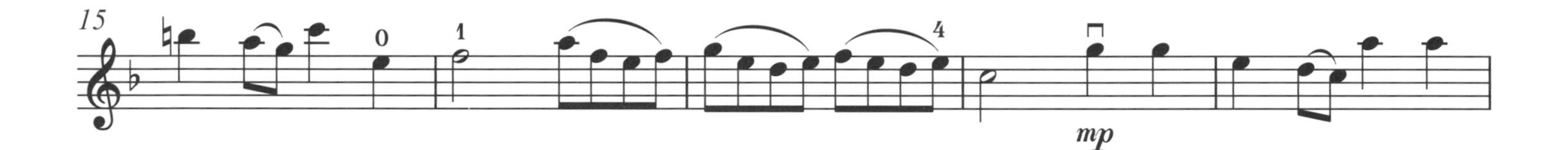

Georg Philipp Telemann was one of the most prolific and versatile German composers of his day. He studied at Leipzig University and held court appointments at Žary and Eisenach before becoming city music director at Frankfurt (1712) and Hamburg (1721). In Frankfurt he directed a local *collegium musicum* (music society) in weekly public concerts at which his own instrumental works were performed. These no doubt included the Six Sonatinas for violin and harpsichord, which were first published in 1718.

The finale of Sonatina No. 6, reproduced here, has an Italian tempo mark but nonetheless resembles the French *gavotte en rondeau*, with its half-bar upbeat, central episode (b. 8) and return of the opening theme (b. 22). Despite the time signature, it is best to think in terms of two minim beats per bar. All the dynamics are editorial suggestions only, as are the violin slurs in bb. 9 and 21. RJ

Source: *Sei Sonatine per violino e cembalo* (Amsterdam: Le Cène, 1724/5)

Adapted from *Baroque Violin Pieces*, Book 2, edited by Richard Jones (ABRSM).

Over the Rainbow

from *The Wizard of Oz*

Arranged by Barnes Music Engraving Ltd

Harold Arlen (1905–86)
and E. Y. Harburg (1896–1981)

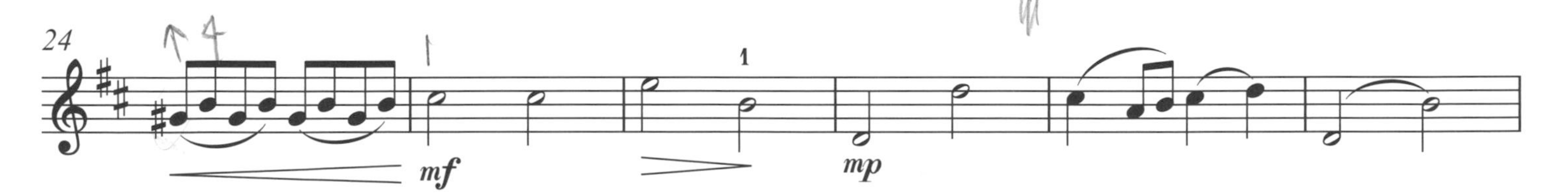

'Over the Rainbow' was voted the No. 1 song of the 20th century in a 2007 poll of the music industry. It comes from the American film *The Wizard of Oz*, released in 1939. Early in the film, young Dorothy, fed up with her existence on a farm in Kansas, imagines travelling to a faraway land 'somewhere over the rainbow' (the words sung to the first line of the melody in bb. 3 and 4). Shortly afterwards, she is carried off by a tornado to the land of Oz, where she encounters witches, a wizard and other strange characters. The song, one of several written for the film by the established team of lyricist E. Y. ('Yip') Harburg and composer Harold Arlen, won an Academy Award (Oscar). It was performed many times by the actress who played Dorothy, Judy Garland, and has also been sung by many other leading artists.

Theme and Variation

from 24 Caprices, Op. 1

Arranged by Christiane Bornemann

Nicolò Paganini
(1782–1840)

In the exam, all repeats should be observed.

Nicolò Paganini, a native of Genoa in northern Italy, was the supreme violin virtuoso of the early 19th century, generating a surge of adulation and wonder in audiences across Europe. In 1820, he published a set of 24 caprices for solo violin. The last of them is a set of variations on a simple and memorable theme – which has also been treated in variation form by many other composers including Liszt, Brahms, Rachmaninoff and Andrew Lloyd Webber. This arrangement consists of the theme and a simplified version of the first variation, with an added piano accompaniment.

The Lark in the Clear Air

B:3

Arranged by T. C. Kelly

Trad. Irish

The Lark in the Clear Air is a traditional Irish song, previously known as *The Tailor's Son* or *Kathleen Nowlan*, for which the 19th-century Irish poet and antiquarian Sir Samuel Ferguson wrote new words, beginning:

> Dear thoughts are in my mind, and my soul soars enchanted,
> As I hear the sweet lark sing in the clear air of the day.

This arrangement, by the Irish composer T. C. Kelly, hints in the piano part at the characteristic playing techniques of the harp, one of the most important instruments in Irish traditional music.

Pig Ankle Rag

for solo violin

Arranged by Pete Cooper

Trad. American

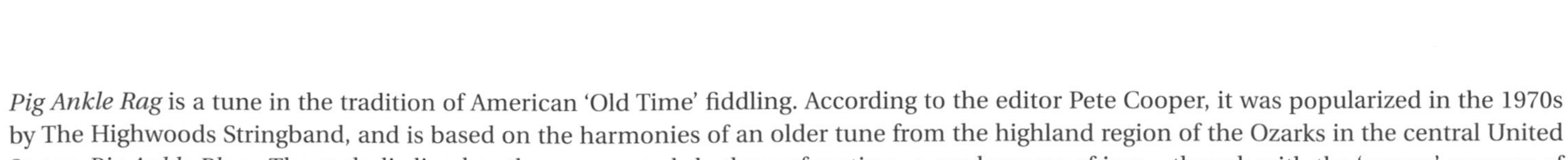

Pig Ankle Rag is a tune in the tradition of American 'Old Time' fiddling. According to the editor Pete Cooper, it was popularized in the 1970s by The Highwoods Stringband, and is based on the harmonies of an older tune from the highland region of the Ozarks in the central United States, *Pig Ankle Blues*. The melodic line has the syncopated rhythms of ragtime, a predecessor of jazz – though with the 'swung' quavers of later idioms.

America

from *West Side Story*

Arranged by Jerry Lanning

Leonard Bernstein (1918–90)
and Stephen Sondheim (born 1930)

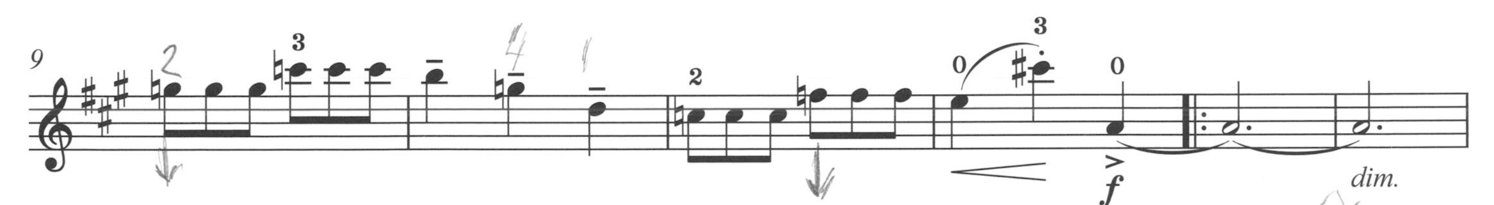

The American musician Leonard Bernstein was not only one of the leading conductors of his time, but also a composer for both the concert hall and the musical theatre. His most successful musical was *West Side Story*, which opened on Broadway in New York in September 1957, ran for nearly two years, and was later made into a film. Originally the conception of choreographer Jerome Robbins, and with lyrics by Stephen Sondheim, it transfers the story of Shakespeare's *Romeo and Juliet* to New York City in the 1950s, where the feuding Montagues and Capulets are replaced by the Jets and the Sharks, rival teenage gangs of white Americans and Puerto Ricans. 'America' is sung by a group of the Sharks' girlfriends, who quarrel exuberantly about the advantages and disadvantages of having moved to New York from their native Caribbean island of Puerto Rico, but who mostly agree, as they sing at the start of the chorus (bb. 5–8):

I like to be in America,
OK by me in America

The song is mostly in the Latin-American dance rhythm of the huapango, in which bars of six quavers alternate between 6/8 and 3/4 metre.

The Folk from the Mountain

Arranged by Edward Huws Jones

Trad. French

The bourrée is best known, for example in the music of J. S. Bach, as a courtly dance in fast duple metre: but in the folk music of the Auvergne region of central France it is usually in triple time. The arranger Edward Huws Jones has brought together in ABA form, as if for continuous dancing, two songs in bourrée rhythm from the Artense district of the Auvergne. The first is called 'Al cuol de Pierron' ('Pierre's Backside'); the second (from b. 25) is 'Les lordaus de la montanha' ('The Folk from the Mountain', or more literally 'The Bumpkins from the Mountain'). The first tune is in three-bar phrases, and the second in four-bar phrases. The tunes are not in major or minor keys but in modes, as can be seen by comparing the apparent key notes with the key signatures. The direction 'like a hurdy-gurdy' suggests very smooth bowing, as the hurdy-gurdy is played by turning a wheel which remains in contact with the strings; the instrument's drone is imitated in the piano part and in some of the optional double-stopping.

Slightly faster

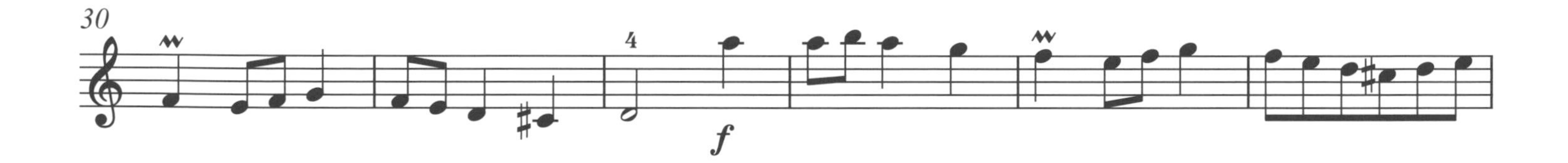